GW00674956

WELCOME TO  VERDANT WORKS

The story of jute and the story of Dundee are inseparable. The industry employed 50,000 people in the city at its peak and supplied much of the world's demand for jute goods. Verdant Works takes you on a tour of the trade, from its beginnings in the Indian subcontinent to the end product in all its myriad forms, and allows you to experience at first hand what life was like for workers in the mill.

WITH A STUNNING RANGE OF DISPLAYS INCLUDING FILM SHOWS, INTERACTIVE COMPUTERS AND ORIGINAL MACHINERY LOVINGLY RESTORED TO WORKING CONDITION, VERDANT WORKS BRINGS HISTORY TO LIFE WITH AN EXPERIENCE YOU WILL NEVER FORGET.

Dundee
VERDANT WORKS

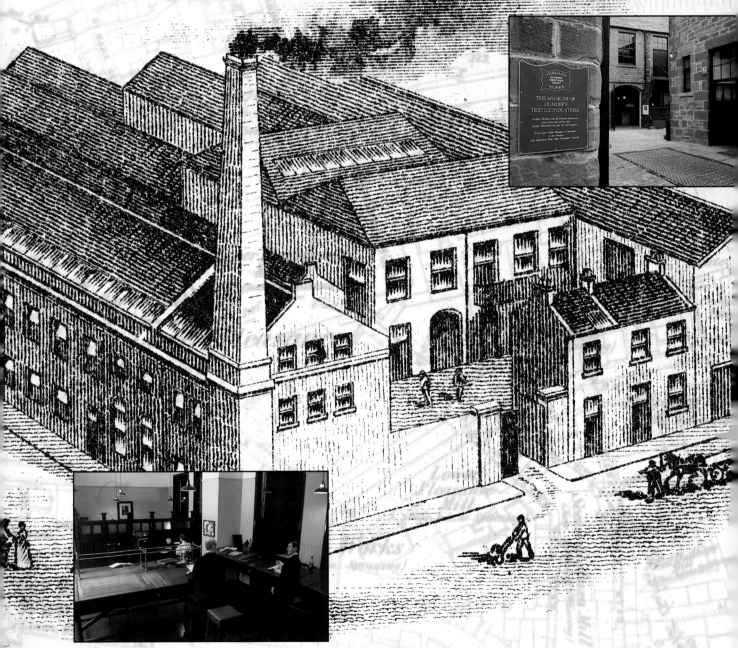

Period Works Office, Verdant Works, 1996

The seemingly incongruous 'green' name of 'Verdant' for a textile works in an industrial area dates back to when Verdant was built. At that time most of the surrounding area was still green fields and nursery grounds.

The High Mill of Verdant Works was built in 1833 for David Lindsay, merchant and flaxspinner. Over the following thirty years further buildings such as warehouses, batching areas and offices were added until the site looked as it does today. Like many Dundee flax mills in the 1840s and 1850s Verdant Works switched to processing jute. Verdant Works was bought in the 1850s by John Ewan, a manufacturer of canvas, sacking, bagging and hessians. Ewan was elected to Dundee Town Council in 1854 and became Provost two years later. By 1864 Verdant Works is recorded as possessing three steam engines driving 70 power looms and 2,800 spindles. A workforce of 500 was employed to prepare and spin jute in the mill and to weave in a separate factory across the road in Milne Street. In comparison with 61 other textile works in the city at this time, Verdant's workforce ranked 16th in size.

By 1889 Verdant's time as a true textile works is over and the name disappears from the lists of mills and factories in the Dundee Directory. In 1893 it reappears under the new ownership of Alexander Thomson & Sons, china and waste merchants and flock manufacturers. Verdant was now used to re-cycle the large amounts of jute waste produced as a by-product of the industry, to cure rabbit skins for the fashion trade and to deal in scrap metals. When Alexander Thomson & Sons sold the business in the 1960s, Verdant became home to a number of different companies until Dundee Heritage Trust bought the site in 1991.

Map of Blackness area, 1874

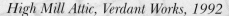
High Mill Attic, Verdant Works, 1992

The lade in the machinery hall

RESTORATION

Verdant Works High Mill Attic, 1991

WHEN DUNDEE HERITAGE TRUST PURCHASED VERDANT WORKS IN 1991 THE SITE WAS IN A DERELICT CONDITION. AT SOME 50,000 SQUARE FEET IN SIZE IT IS NOT ONE OF THE LARGEST JUTE MILLS IN DUNDEE BUT IT WAS A HUGE BUILDING TO RESTORE NEVERTHELESS.

Verdant Works is a rare surviving example of a courtyard type mill, meriting its category 'A' listing as a building of national architectural importance. Verdant Works was relatively un-modernised when Dundee Heritage Trust bought it and a host of original features remained.

The clean -up begins, 1991

We are undertaking a programme of sympathetic restoration which aims to retain the character of the original building. Wherever possible we use appropriate historic materials and methods, while still meeting modern standards in fire safety, security and access.

Exterior of the High Mill, 1991

There is always an element of industrial archaeology when building work starts, as we never quite know what we might find. Hidden underneath the floor was a lade - a stone channel used to divert water from the Scouring Burn for a mill's power needs.

Building work, 1992

Verdant Works was opened on 16 September 1996 by The Rt. Hon. Lord Younger of Prestwick. The second and final phase of the textile museum was opened exactly a year later by the Prime Minister of The People's Republic of Bangladesh, The Hon. Sheikh Hasina.

Verdant Works, 1996

WHY *Dundee & Jute?*

COARSE LINEN was already being made locally into the sort of products jute could also be used for.

WORKERS in flax had the necessary skills to adapt to the similar methods and machines of jute processing.

THE BOUNTY, a subsidy paid to encourage the manufacture of linen was removed. This made other fibres such as jute potentially more profitable.

STAMPING of linen cloth ceased. This ending of quality control encouraged manufacturers to experiment with other fibres.

FLAX SUPPLIES became unreliable and expensive as wartime blockades closed the Baltic ports.

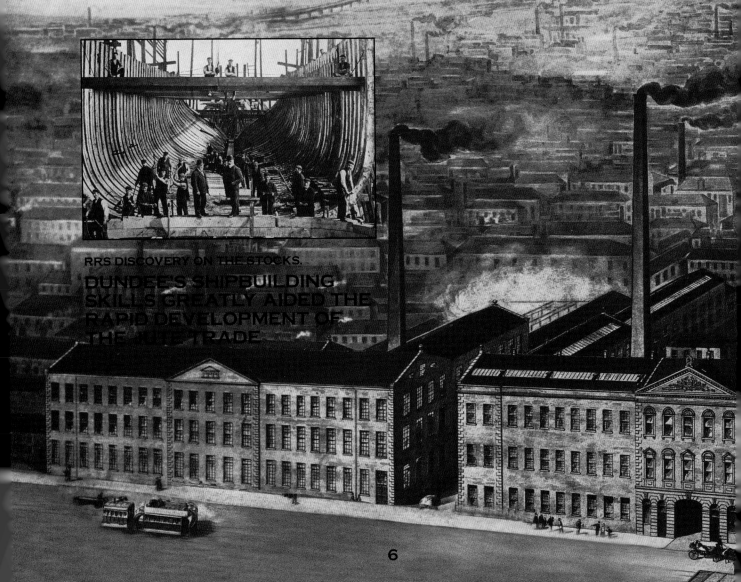

RRS DISCOVERY ON THE STOCKS.
DUNDEE'S SHIPBUILDING
SKILLS GREATLY AIDED THE
RAPID DEVELOPMENT OF
THE JUTE TRADE

WHALE OIL for softening jute was easily available from the local whaling fleet.

GEOGRAPHIC LOCATION meant good trading connections.

SHIPBUILDING SKILLS meant Dundee could build the big, fast ships to transport the jute from India.

ENTERPRISING MERCHANT COMMUNITY looking for new, cheaper alternatives to flax.

EAST INDIA COMPANY was looking for new markets for raw jute.

GROWTH IN WORLD TRADE led to a huge demand for the products of jute, especially sacking and baling materials.

The arrival of the power loom and the start of the factory system rapidly changed a whole way of life for the people of Dundee. The home-based textile industry was unable to resist the major technological progress and the handloom weavers' wages were gradually worn down by the competition. They struggled to survive on the margins of industrial society, relying on those few jobs that were beyond the capabilities of the power looms.

PRIOR TO

MECHANISATION

JUTE FABRIC WAS
PRODUCED ON HANDLOOMS

GROWING JUTE

Jute is an annual crop, sown between February and June.

Over a period of 4 to 6 months the plant grows to a height of 3-5 metres.

Taking jute to market

Retting jute

Harvesting jute

Stripping and washing jute

From July to October the plants are harvested by hand-sickle and tied into bundles until the leaves fall off. Now the fibre extraction process of 'retting' begins. The reeds are soaked in water for 10 to 12 days until the fibres can easily be separated from the stalks. The extracted fibres are then washed and hung up to dry on bamboo rails. Jute for export is made into 'pucca' bales weighing 400 lbs.

WHAT IS JUTE?

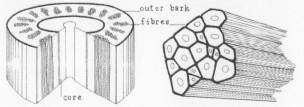

Jute is a bast fibre, a vegetable fibre composed of cellulose. Bast fibre grows the entire length of the plant stalk from root to tip. Groups of fibres are contained in the pithy layer between the thin outer bark and the woody core. The two other bast fibres traditionally spun in Dundee were flax and hemp.

Raw jute fibre is obtained from the stems of two varieties of plant: *Corchorus capsularis* and *Corchorus olitorius*, both of which are grown mainly around the delta of the Ganges and the Brahmaputra rivers in what was the state of Eastern Bengal in India.

Raw jute fibre was first imported into Britain in 1791 by the East India Company which traded in Bengal where the fibre was hand-twisted and woven into a coarse cloth. Jute proved to be difficult to spin by machine because of its brittleness - then the discovery was made in Dundee that the fibre could be softened by soaking it with oil and water. The Dundee whaling fleet provided ample supplies of whale oil for this process. Jute was first spun successfully in the early 1830s and by the 1850s it had surpassed flax as the dominant fibre processed in the city.

THE CLIPPER SHIPS

THE GROWTH OF THE JUTE INDUSTRY LED TO AN INCREASED DEMAND FOR IMPORTED RAW MATERIALS. THIS ENCOURAGED THE EXPANSION OF THE CITY'S HARBOUR AND THE SHIPBUILDING INDUSTRY.

IN 1882 THE CLIPPER SHIP S.S. LOCHEE MADE THE VOYAGE FROM CALCUTTA TO DUNDEE IN A RECORD 90 DAYS, CUTTING 30 DAYS OFF THE NORMAL VOYAGE TIME.

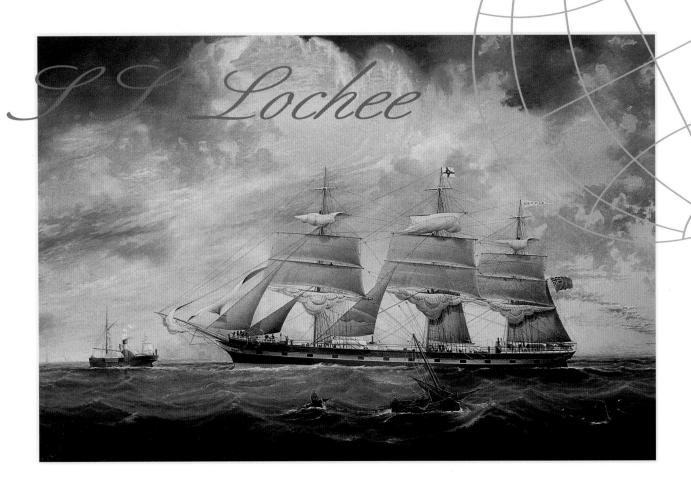

The first Indian jute mill was established in 1855 in Serampore using machinery and workers from Dundee. The mill benefited from cheap labour and closeness to the raw material. Rapid development followed and mills and factories sprang up along the banks of the River Hooghly.

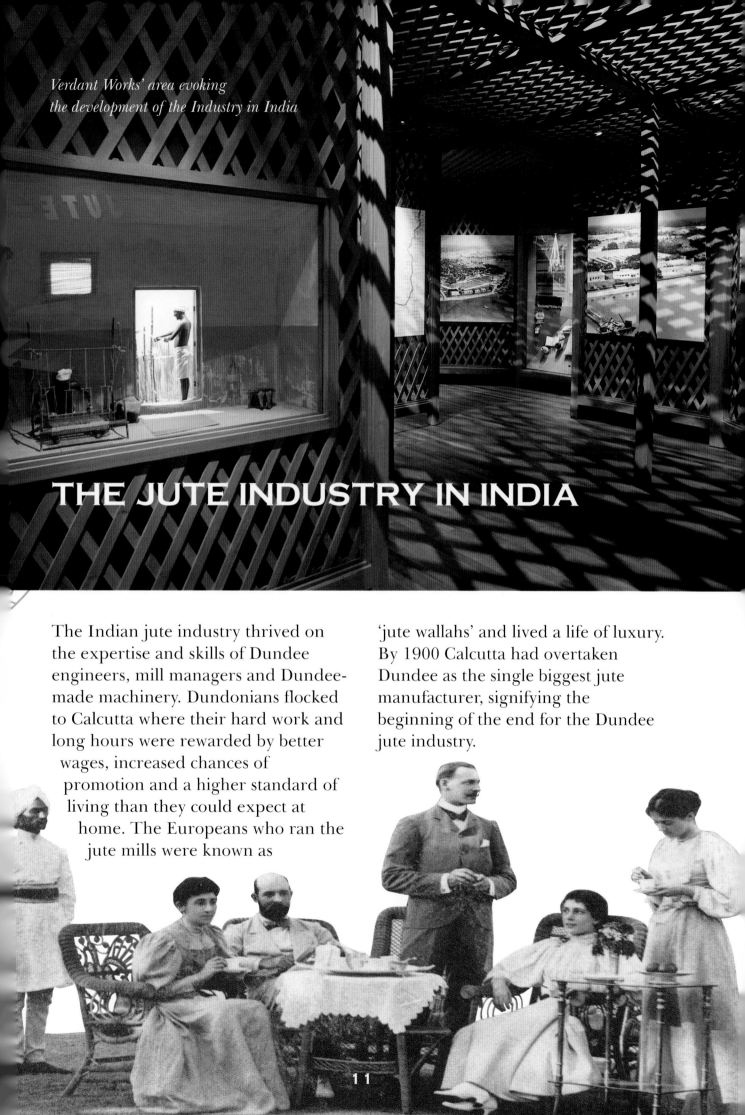

Verdant Works' area evoking the development of the Industry in India

THE JUTE INDUSTRY IN INDIA

The Indian jute industry thrived on the expertise and skills of Dundee engineers, mill managers and Dundee-made machinery. Dundonians flocked to Calcutta where their hard work and long hours were rewarded by better wages, increased chances of promotion and a higher standard of living than they could expect at home. The Europeans who ran the jute mills were known as 'jute wallahs' and lived a life of luxury. By 1900 Calcutta had overtaken Dundee as the single biggest jute manufacturer, signifying the beginning of the end for the Dundee jute industry.

Machinery in
the former raw jute
warehouse

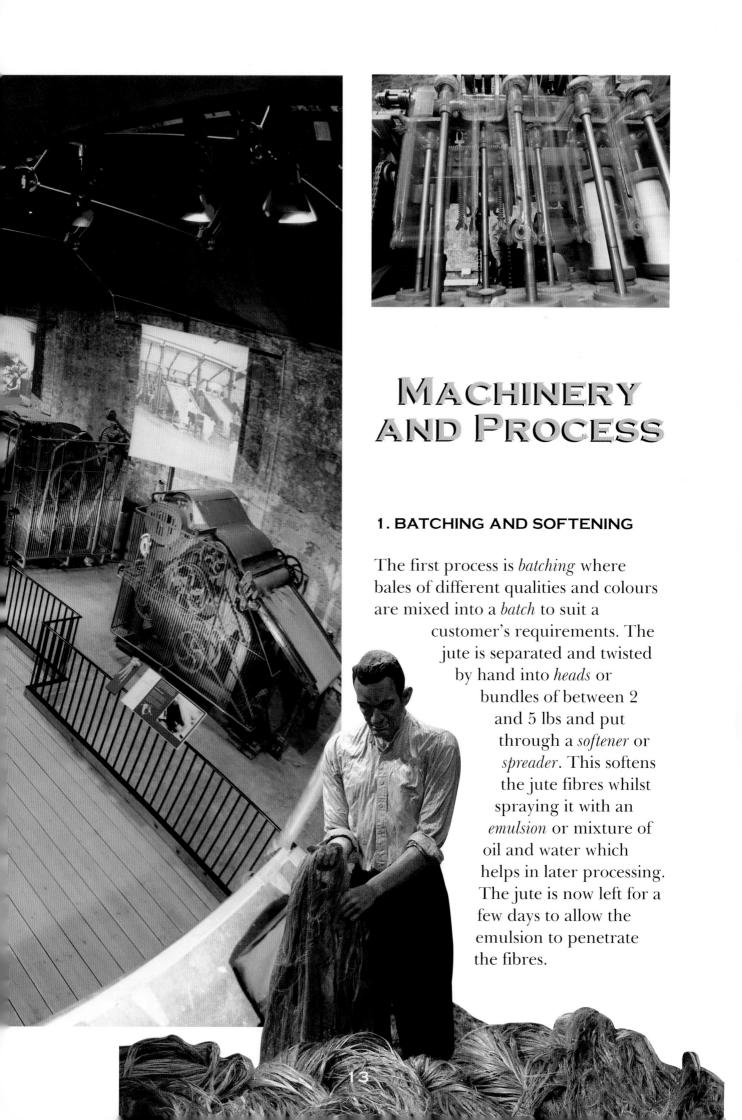

MACHINERY AND PROCESS

1. BATCHING AND SOFTENING

The first process is *batching* where bales of different qualities and colours are mixed into a *batch* to suit a customer's requirements. The jute is separated and twisted by hand into *heads* or bundles of between 2 and 5 lbs and put through a *softener* or *spreader*. This softens the jute fibres whilst spraying it with an *emulsion* or mixture of oil and water which helps in later processing. The jute is now left for a few days to allow the emulsion to penetrate the fibres.

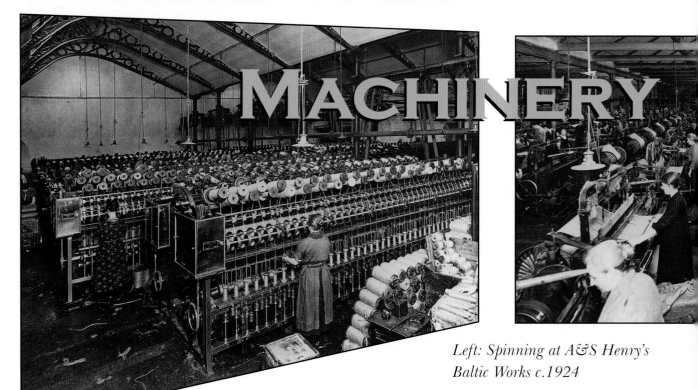

Left: Spinning at A&S Henry's Baltic Works c.1924

2. CARDING

Carding machines consist of a series of rollers revolving at different speeds with projecting metal pins called *hackles* on them. Their combing action *fleeces* the jute before condensing it into a loose fibre called *sliver*. Carding also further mixes the fibres, with the jute now of a more even colour and quality.

3. DRAWING

The drawing frames make the sliver more uniform, straighten the fibres and reduce it to a suitable size and weight for spinning. The sliver is now uniform with the fibres lying in parallel to the line of sliver.

4. ROVING

Roving machines draw out the sliver further to a suitable size for spinning. As the resulting sliver is delicate, a slight twist is added which gives it strength for the spinning process. The twisted rove is then wound onto a *bobbin* for transfer to the spinning frame.

5. SPINNING

Spinning frames draw or draft the fibres to the specified thickness or *count*, twist the fibres to bind them together into a continuous thread and wind the resulting yarn onto bobbins.

6. COP AND SPOOL WINDING

Bobbins from the spinning frames are passed to the winding department where the yarn on them is wound onto *spools* to provide the *warp* thread and onto *cops* which fit into the shuttle and supply the *weft* thread for weaving.

7. BEAMING

The spools from the winding department are loaded onto a framework called a *bank* from which the threads are drawn and wound onto the

The Finisher Card

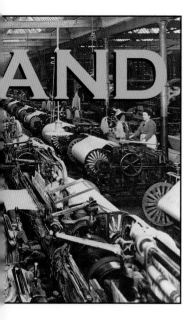

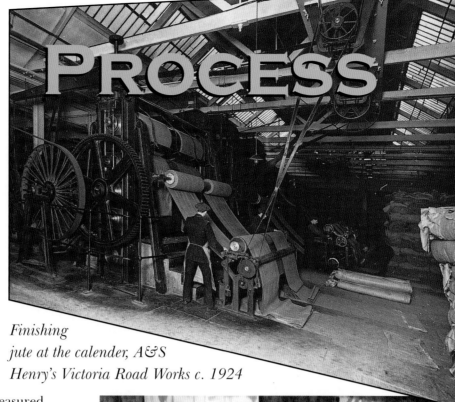

Weaving at A&S Henry's Baltic Works c. 1924

Finishing jute at the calender, A&S Henry's Victoria Road Works c. 1924

wooden reel or *swift* to a measured length. The ends from the swift are taken through the separating reed, then a tensioning roller and tied into the beam. The beam is set in motion and this pulls the ends onto it, ready for fitting to the back of the loom.

8. WEAVING

Weaving is carried out on looms. The shuttle carrying the weft thread is picked backwards and forwards across the loom by a picking arm, interlacing the weft with the warp threads. The warp threads which are raised and lowered are drawn from the back of the beam.

9. FINISHING

If a high quality product is required the cloth is sent to the finishing department where it is *cropped* to shear off surplus fibres. The cloth is then *calendered* by being passed under intense pressure through heavy rollers to give a smooth and pressed finish.

Servant of INDUSTRY

Dundee's fame spread far and wide as the products of her mills were exported all around the world. Jute's appeal lay in its strength, low cost, durability and versatility. Uses included sacking, tarpaulins, carpet backing, lining upholstery, roofing felts, tents and sand bags.

The pioneers in the United States benefited from Dundee jute and linen products

Jute was used for a number of unusual products including clothing and 'parajutes'. During the Second World War jute was used as an emergency stand-in fabric to make parachutes for dropping supplies. Jute hessian is still used as a backing for linoleum and the highest quality carpets such as Axminster and Wilton.

JUTE PRODUCTS

Aprons
Bags
Boot linings
Carpets
Cattle bedding
Chairs
Coal bags
Electric cable

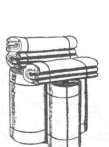

Jute sacks being used at a sugar refinery in Sydney, Australia - in some cases the sacks are stacked up to 70 tiers high

Fuse yarns
Garden twines
Hessians
Horse covers
Linoleum backings
Mattresses
Meat wrappers
Nail bagging
Oven cloths
Ropes
Rugs
Parachutes
Sacking
Sailcloth
Satchels
Scrims
String
Tapestries
Tarpaulins
Tents
Webbing
Wrappers for bacon
Yarns

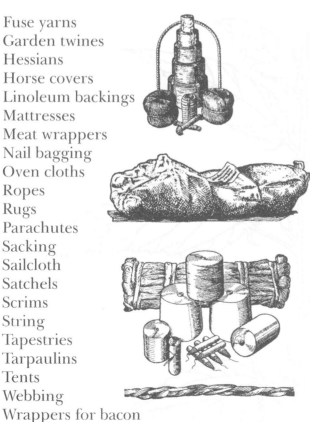

ROPE

JUTE IS USED TO MAKE ROPE BECAUSE IT IS STRONG, HEAVY AND ALLOWS A GOOD GRIP. IN 1884-5 DUNDEE HAD 20 ROPE MAKERS PRODUCING THE VAST AMOUNTS OF ROPE NEEDED BY THE CITY'S SHIPS.

THE DECLINE OF THE JUTE INDUSTRY

and

POLY
PROPYLENE

The Dundee jute industry began to decline from the beginning of the 20th century due to fierce competition from the Indian jute industry. Despite periods of boom during the two world wars Dundee could not keep pace with the rate of production overseas. By 1950 there were only 39 jute firms left out of a total of 150 at the industry's peak.

By 1998 only one true jute spinning mill survived in Dundee, Tay Spinners of Taybank Works.

Polypropylene, a high-tech plastic fibre derived from oil became a substitute for some of jute's main products from the mid-1960s. Tayside entered a new phase in its role as a centre of excellence in the textile industry and is now one of the world's premier suppliers of polypropylene products. Some of the long established textile companies made the successful transition from linen to jute and then to polypropylene processing.

MILLS

Many buildings of Dundee's jute industry still stand as monuments to the city's proud manufacturing past. They have been converted to alternative uses ranging from warehouses to nightclubs. Some of the most successful conversions have been to housing.

Beefcan Close, Dundee

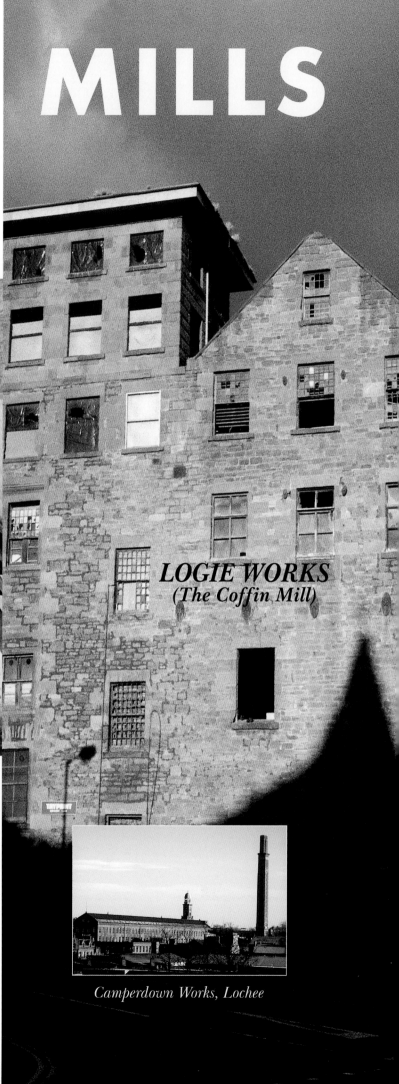

LOGIE WORKS
(The Coffin Mill)

IT IS IRONIC THAT THE MILLS ARE NOW PROVIDING HIGH QUALITY ACCOMMODATION, SOMETHING WHICH THEIR PAST WORKERS DID NOT HAVE.

Camperdown Works, Lochee

HARD

WORKING CONDITIONS

The wage rates in the jute industry were among the lowest in Scotland. Poor employment laws offered the workers little protection from the hardship of factory life. People worked long exhausting hours. In 1833 boys might work 18 or 19 hours a day in some flax mills. Often children fell asleep over their work which increased the likelihood of industrial accidents. A great deal of dust or *stour* was created in the mill, covering people from head to toe, clogging mouths and noses.

The number of people in a confined place, combined with the heat, dust and fumes of oil and grease, caused a condition known as 'Mill Fever', and encouraged respiratory diseases like bronchitis. Working long hours in close proximity to extremely noisy machinery resulted in many workers going deaf.

WORK

ACCIDENTS

ACCIDENTS AT VERDANT

26/3/1852
'FATAL ACCIDENT: ON TUESDAY AFTERNOON A GIRL EMPLOYED IN VERDANT MILL GOT ENTANGLED ABOUT A CARDING MACHINE AND SUSTAINED SUCH INJURIES BEFORE SHE COULD BE RELEASED AS TO OCCASION INSTANTANEOUS DEATH.'

4/3/1853 'ACCIDENTAL DEATH: WE REGRET TO RECORD THE DEATH OF JAMES CLARK A WORKER AT VERDANT MILL WHICH TOOK PLACE ON WEDNESDAY EVENING, IN CONSEQUENCE OF AN ACCIDENT WHICH HAPPENED TO HIM WHILE ATTENDING HIS EMPLOYMENT ON THE PREVIOUS DAY. IT APPEARS HE WAS CAUGHT BY A BELT OF THE MACHINERY WHICH CARRIED HIM RAPIDLY TO THE ROOF OF THE BUILDING WHERE HE WAS THREE TIMES REVOLVED ROUND ONE OF THE SHAFTS BEFORE HE COULD BE EXTRICATED. HE WAS CONVEYED TO THE INFIRMARY AS SOON AS POSSIBLE, BUT THE POOR FELLOW WAS SO MUCH BRUISED THAT DEATH WAS THE RESULT'.

ONE OF MANY FIRES

21 AUGUST 1840 THE DUNDEE, PERTH AND CUPAR ADVERTISER REPORTS A DREADFUL CONFLAGRATION AT MR LINDSAY'S MILL IN HENDERSON'S WYND. IT STARTED ABOUT 4.30 IN THE SOUTH-EAST WING AND SPREAD TO THE MAIN BUILDING BEFORE THE FIRE ENGINES ARRIVED. IT SPREAD RAPIDLY WESTWARD UNTIL THE ENTIRE BUILDING WAS ONE SHEET OF FLAME. ROOF OF NORTH AND SOUTH BUILDINGS FELL IN AND FIRE SPREAD TO THE FOUNDATION STOREY. THE FIRE DID NOT REACH THE ENGINE-HOUSE, SAVED WITH ITS CONTENTS. THE BUILDING AND MACHINERY, WHICH COST UPWARDS OF £20,000, ARE ENTIRELY DESTROYED. THE LOSS TO MR LINDSAY ON THIS OCCASION IS VERY GREAT, BUT NOT MORE SO THAN TO THE NUMEROUS PEOPLE EMPLOYED AT HIS WORKS, WHICH WE UNDERSTAND WERE NOT LESS THAN 200. IN THE PRESENT DEPRESSED STATE OF TRADE IT WILL BE DIFFICULT FOR THEM TO OBTAIN EMPLOYMENT ELSEWHERE, BUT WE TRUST THAT A GENEROUS PUBLIC WILL LOOK AFTER THEIR WANTS!

LIVING CONDITIONS

The Plettie

Housing in the Hilltown, early 20th century

Large numbers of workers lived in tenements close to the mill or factory. Dundee had a reputation for poor housing. In 1911 about 70% of the dwellings in Dundee were of only one or two rooms and overcrowding was common. The average number of people living in a home was eight. Families slept in box beds, often sharing four to a bed. Public wells supplying polluted water and privies that emptied directly onto the streets all contributed to the cholera and typhus epidemics that swept the city in the 19th century. The addition of '*stairheid cludgies*' or toilets on the stair towers that were shared by many families was a great improvement, but still primitive by today's health standards.

HEALTH

By the beginning of the 20th century, '*convenience*' foods such as margarine, white bread and sugar were replacing the traditional foodstuffs of oatmeal, bone broth and potatoes. This food could be prepared in tenements with limited cooking facilities and prepared quickly - a necessity when so many women worked. The result was a poorer diet but a higher amount of the weekly budget being spent on food. Infant mortality rates in Dundee were very high with a third of all children dying before their first birthday. Those who did survive suffered poor health and had a short life expectancy.
In 1904 over 50% of the Dundee men who appeared as volunteers at the army recruitment office were deemed unfit for military service.

CHILDREN

Thousands of children were employed in Dundee's textile mills. Out of 30,000 workers in 1883 about one fifth were under 15 years of age. Children were paid very low wages and the machines could be placed closer together if little bodies cleaned and maintained them. Children under nine worked as '*pickers*' cleaning away the dust on the underside of machinery, sometimes only two and a half feet from the floor. They worked very long hours for wages which were a vital part of their families' income.

Factory reforms in 1833 required children to attend school two hours daily for 6 days a week. These children, who divided their time between mill and school became known as half-timers.

LONG HOURS
LOW WAGES

MILL GIRLS

Dundee was known as '*a woman's town*' or '*she town*' due to the dominance of women in the labour market. In the jute mills they outnumbered men by three to one. A unique breed of women evolved from the hardship of life in the mills and the responsibility of being the main provider for the family. Dundee women gained the freedom to act in a way which often ignored convention. They were '*Over-dressed, loud, bold-eyed girls*' according to one observer and the sight of a woman being as '*roarin' fou*' or drunk as a man was commonplace.

However, despite the undoubted hardships, former mill girls often recall their working days with fondness. Great friendships were made in the mills and people looked out for one another.

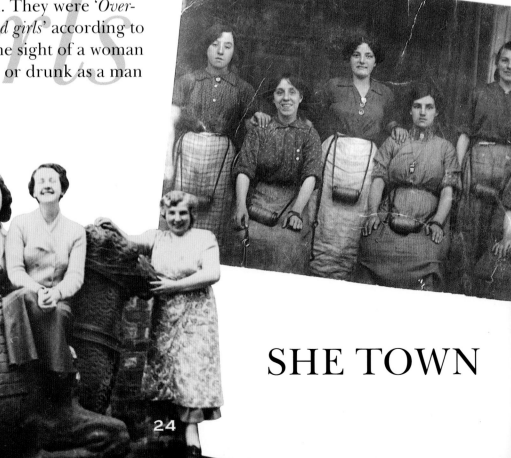

SHE TOWN

SUFFRAGETTES

*"I canna see why a woman who is clever enough
to earn money to pay her taxes like a man canna go and put a cross
on a sheet of paper once every five years or so."*

Working class women formed the bedrock of the suffrage movement in
Dundee and jute workers took an active part in the struggle for the vote.

Unions and Strikes

The Dundee and District Mill & Factory Operatives Union was formed in 1885
and soon had a membership of 6,000, the majority of whom were women.
Generally, workers were reluctant to strike when unemployment rates were high
because there would be plenty of desperate workers willing to take their places.
The most dramatic action was The Great Strike of 1874 when up to 30,000
workers protested for four days at a decision to reduce wages by 10%. Eventually a
lesser reduction of 5% was agreed to by most mill owners.

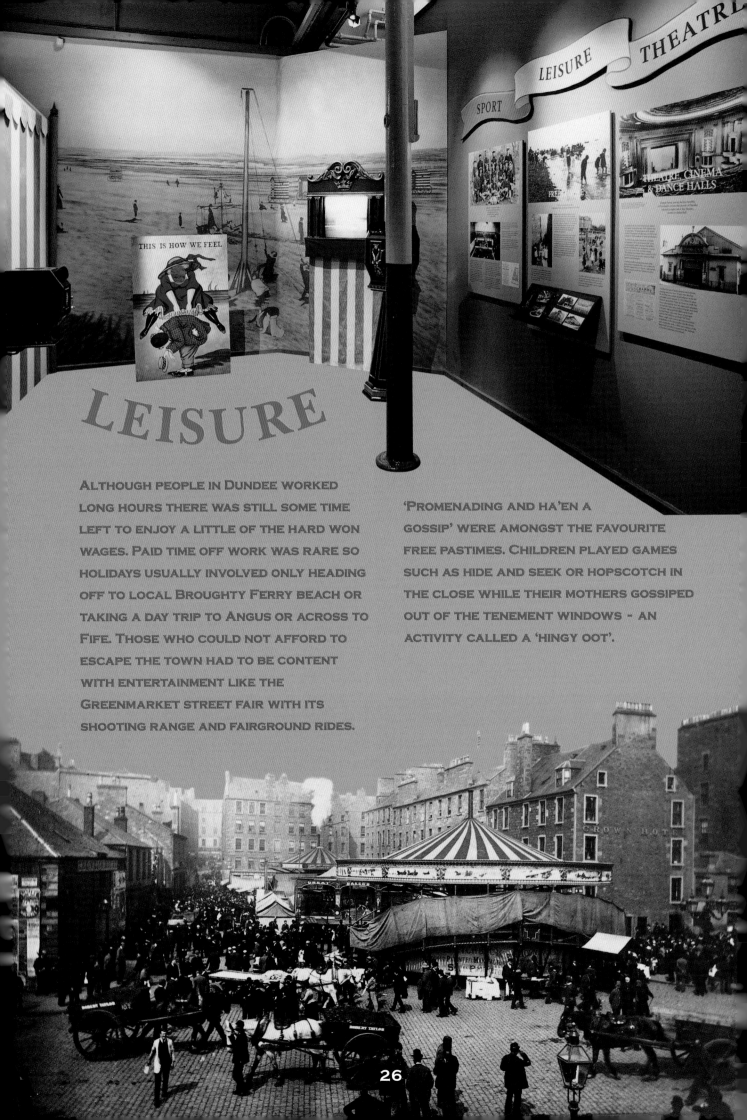

THIS IS HOW WE FEEL

SPORT LEISURE THEATRE

THEATRE, CINEMA
& DANCE HALLS

LEISURE

Although people in Dundee worked long hours there was still some time left to enjoy a little of the hard won wages. Paid time off work was rare so holidays usually involved only heading off to local Broughty Ferry beach or taking a day trip to Angus or across to Fife. Those who could not afford to escape the town had to be content with entertainment like the Greenmarket street fair with its shooting range and fairground rides.

'Promenading and ha'en a gossip' were amongst the favourite free pastimes. Children played games such as hide and seek or hopscotch in the close while their mothers gossiped out of the tenement windows - an activity called a 'hingy oot'.

LEISURE

New parks, libraries and swimming baths, provided by the mill owners, improved the quality of life for Dundonians. Theatre, dance halls and cinema provided an escape from some of the grim realities of industrial life. Cox's workers who had left Camperdown at 5.30pm could regularly be seen queuing outside the Astoria in Lochee before 6pm. Dundonians were attracted to outdoor pursuits in an attempt to escape from the unhealthy air and stifling conditions in the jute mills. The 19th century saw a vast increase in sports from running to swimming and boxing. Football gained a hold in the late 19th century, becoming a hugely popular spectator sport and a game played by hundreds of Dundonians at amateur level.

The Greenmarket in full swing

DRUNKENNESS

'So long as workers' homes exhibit the extreme discomfort and cheerlessness which is so frequent and marked a feature, the inmates will welcome any means of escape and at present the public houses are the readiest and most persistent attraction.' (Dundee Social Union Report, 1905). Victorian Dundee had a serious problem with drunkenness as people drank to forget their misery and escape their problems. Working class women in the jute trade were notorious for bouts of heavy drinking.

Drunkenness was a major cause of crime and social problems in the city. Money spent on drink was also money not spent on basic rent or food, leaving families without enough to live on.

There were plenty of places to drink. By 1846 Dundee had one pub to every 24 families and in the early days the pubs were open from 8am until 11pm. In 1897 Dundee had no fewer than 7 breweries and 186 licensed bars.

THE JUTE *Barons*

PHILANTHROPY

Dundee had a vast working-class community but at the very top of society was a small group of wealthy families, the owners of the jute mills. The '*Jute Barons*' lived in large mansions in Broughty Ferry or in the countryside away from the oppressive and polluted environment of the city. They had a great deal of influence and dedicated substantial amounts of their time and money to serving the community and improving the city's facilities.

Many people have argued that the money from the 'Barons' would have been better spent on providing quality housing and sanitation for their workers.

Opening of Baxter Park 1863

Sir David Baxter of Dens Works gifted £50,000 (equivalent today to £2.5 million) to create Baxter Park with its beautiful pavilion. Sir James Caird of Ashton Works donated £100,000 (around £5 million today) to create a new City Hall and concert hall for Dundee - the Caird Hall.

Castleroy Broughty Ferry - home of the Gilroy family of Tay Works

Jute Barons

Sir James Caird

SERVICES

SHOP AT THE WORKS

The souvenir shop carries a wide range of quality gifts in all price ranges. Many items are exclusive to Verdant Works, some are even made from jute woven in the museum.

There is always something new and exciting happening at Verdant Works. The Special Exhibition Gallery has a programme of changing displays and throughout the year we run a series of special events and activities.

CAFE

The Cafe serves morning coffee, snacks, light lunches and afternoon teas.

VERDANT WORKS

CONFERENCE FACILITIES

Verdant Works is a conference venue with a difference. Comfortable facilities, a warm welcome and historic surroundings make Verdant Works ideal for functions and conferences for up to 70 people.

EDUCATION SERVICES

School parties of all ages are welcome at Verdant Works. There is an Education Suite where children can participate in pre-arranged activities, project work or eat their packed lunches.

A comprehensive education pack is available and teachers are invited to book a complimentary reconnaissance visit prior to their school trip.

EDUCATION

DUNDEE HERITAGE TRUST

Dundee Heritage Trust was formed as a charity in 1985 to preserve and present Dundee's industrial past. Trustees are drawn from a diverse range of community and business interests in Dundee and Tayside and the Trust has been generously supported by public bodies, local industry and individual benefactors. As well as the textile museum at Verdant Works, Dundee Heritage Trust has responsibility for one of the nation's most important historic ships - RRS Discovery.

The restoration of the ship and the opening of Discovery Point in 1993 were the culmination of many years' effort by the Trust. At Discovery Point you'll find the same amazing mix of interactive exhibits, informative displays and dramatic film shows that let you re-live the epic voyage of Scott of the Antarctic. RRS Discovery is moored alongside the Centre for you to explore.

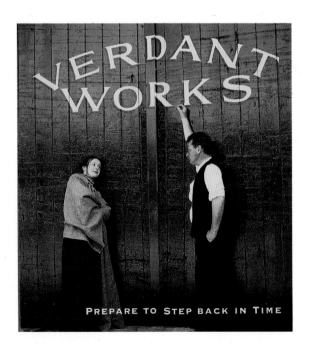